FOURTH ESTATE presents   **BRYAN LEE O'MALLEY's**

RIM
TOGETHER
THOSE TWO MAKE MY MOUTH TASTE LIKE THROW-UP.
THIS IS PROBABLY THE ONLY TIME I'LL EVER AGREE WITH YOU, BUT... I AGREE WITH YOU.

NO SHENANIGANS AT MY PARTY, BITCHES!

HOW IS IT *YOUR* PARTY? I THOUGHT IT WAS STEPHEN STILLS' BIRTHDAY.

MINE WAS LAST TUESDAY AND JULIE'S IS NEXT TUESDAY, SO HERS IS TECHNICALLY ACTIVE.

YEAH, AND *MY* AUNT IS LETTING US USE HER HOUSE IN THE BEACHES, *KIM.*

WHOOP-DE-DOO.

ARE YOU WELL?

DO YOU HAVE BRAIN DAMAGE?

DID ANYONE SEE WHAT HIT ME?

WOW, NO. IT MUST HAVE BEEN *HUGE.*

HEY, NEIL, WHY AREN'T YOU HANGING OUT WITH KNIVES?

I DON'T WANT TO TALK ABOUT IT.

WHERE IS SHE?

OVER THERE.

KNIVES CHAU
(still 17 years old)

SCOTT...

I THINK YOU'RE THE NICEST GUY I'VE EVER DATED.

THAT'S KIND OF SAD.

Sigh

IT'S PATHETIC!

WHO THE HELL ASKED YOU?!

BACK OFF, BITCH, IT'S MY *BIRTHDAY*.

WELL, I'M DEPRESSED NOW.

HOW'S YOUR BURGER?

edited by James Lucas Jones
design and layout by Bryan Lee O'Malley
production assistance from Steven Birch @ Servo

Published by Fourth Estate

4

Originally published in 2007 in the United States by Oni Press
www.onipress.com

First published in Great Britain in 2010 by
Fourth Estate
An imprint of HarperCollins*Pub ishers*
1 London Bridge Street
London SE1 9GF
www.4thestate.co.uk
Harper CollinsPublishers
1st Floor, Watermarque Building, Ringsend Road
Dublin 4, Ireland
Special thanks to: Hope, the Oni boyz (DOUG!!), Gitter, E. W. Jr., Michael B., my peeps in
Toronto and London, the Halifax crew and the HGPA, mom & dad, bro & sis, kitties, Kanye West,
Clark and Michael . . . and YOU! Winners don't use drugs, expect Claritin this time of year.

www.scottpilgrim.com

10

Printed and bound by CPI
Group (UK) Ltd, Croydon

ISBN: **978-0-00-793082-1**

WOOOOO!!

THANKS.

YOU KNOW, THAT SONG REALLY PISSES ME OFF.

YEAH? I PLAYED IT JUST FOR YOU. HAPPY BIRTHDAY, BABY.

STEPHEN, MOST OF YOUR SONGS JUST BORE ME TO TEARS, BUT THAT ONE—

THE SONG IS ABOUT ME, PEOPLE! HE THINKS I'M A TOTAL BITCH AND A HALF!

GASP.

YOU MEAN SHE DOESN'T KNOW?

BUT IT'S SUCH A GOOD SONG! YOU'RE MISSING THE *TENDERNESS.*

THE NARRATOR IS SAD AND HURT, SEE? BUT THE GIRL THINKS IT'S ALL ABOUT HER!

DON'T YOU GET IT?? IT'S BRILLIANT!!!

UH-HUH.

SHOULD WE BE LETTING HER DRINK BEER?

BLUSH

OKAY, UH... LET'S PLAY ANOTHER ONE.

Julie's aunt's house (later)

knives chau

kim pine

drunk & making out!!

FIND 'EM?

NOPE!! I GUESS THEY WENT HOME!!

Let us never speak of this again

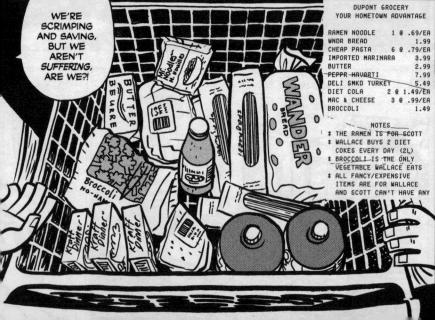

MOVING DAY:
Kim Pine

RIIING

RIIING

RIIING

RII—

HELLO?

SCOTT! GET OUT OF BED!

WHA...? WALLACE...?

THERE'S A HEAT WAVE WARNING IN EFFECT, SO I'M ORDERING YOU TO GET OUT OF OUR FURNACE-LIKE APARTMENT AND GO SOMEWHERE AIR-CONDITIONED LEST YOU DIE.

HEAT WAVE...?

OH, YEAH, I GUESS I'M DRENCHED IN SWEAT...

20
The new hotness

GO SOMEPLACE COOL! OR, YOU KNOW, MAYBE YOU COULD FIND A JOB OR SOMETHING. I HAVE TO GO, OKAY?
CLICK

The Dufferin Mall
(not a particularly exciting mall)

HE'S KINDA CUTE, EH?

EWW, ARE YOU KIDDING ME? HE'S LIKE 25...

TAP TAP TAP

THIRST

CONTENTS OF SCOTT PILGRIM'S POCKETS:

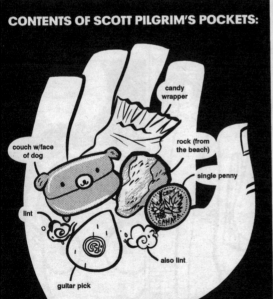

candy wrapper

couch w/face of dog

rock (from the beach)

single penny

lint

also lint

guitar pick

THIRST

THIRST
CASH

SCOTT...?

OH MAN, REMEMBER HOW YOU MOVED AWAY AND KIM WAS ALL—

HEY, HAVE YOU *SEEN* KIM? IS SHE STILL AT NIPISSING? I'M SO OUT OF TOUCH...

OKAY, UH, UM, KIM LIVES IN TORONTO NOW AND WE HANG OUT AND IT'S COOL BUT I... I HAVE A GIRLFRIEND.

YOU DO?! WHAT'S HER NAME? DOES KIM LIKE HER? IS SHE FROM TORONTO?

UH, HER NAME'S RAMONA AND SHE'S FROM AMERICA.

I MEAN, SHE'S AMERICAN.

DID I TELL YOU THAT I'M TOTALLY MOVING TO CALIFORNIA SOON? I HAVE TO HANG AROUND HERE FOR A WHILE, THOUGH.

I'VE BEEN STAYING WITH MY SISTER, SHE HAS A PLACE ON COLLEGE....

DO YOU... UH... HAVE A JOB? I KEEP GETTING ASKED THAT QUESTION, SO...

NAH, I'M JUST BUMMING AROUND. I KNOW, SHOPPING SPREE, RIGHT?

Silk & Satin

THE BODY SHOP

I'M A TOTAL CREDIT CARD MANIAC THESE DAYS, IT'S PATHETIC.

HEY, HAVE YOU EATEN? LET'S GET SOME MALL FOOD, MAN!

21

Getting it together

Coffee chain
(St. Clair location)
Julie & Stacey both work here.

SECOND CUP

SCOTT!

ARE YOU GOING TO WORK? DO YOU HAVE WHAT IT TAKES TO BE A *SERIOUS* DISHWASHER? MAYBE THE BEST DISHWASHER THERE EVER WAS?

I CAN DO IT! *I CAN DO ANYTHING!!* JUST GIVE ME A CHANCE!

HEY, DOMINIQUE? CAN MY FRIEND HAVE THAT JOB?

Subspace
Ramona works here.

And so.

CANADA WAS NEVER SUPPOSED TO GET THIS HOT, DUDE.

YOU PROBABLY THOUGHT WE ALL LIVED IN IGLOOS AND STUFF, RIGHT? WHERE'S YOUR FASHIONABLE PARKA?

SHUT UP.

WHY ARE YOU WEARING THOSE WRIST-BAND THINGS, ANYWAY? DON'T THEY MAKE YOU SWEAT?

NO WAY! THEY KEEP ME *COOL*.

I MEAN...

I... UH...

NO, YOU'RE RIGHT, THAT IS BETTER.

72

In the studio.
(it's actually just Joseph's bedroom)

WAS THAT GOOD?

THAT WAS AWFUL.

SO I SHOULD DO IT AGAIN?

I'M SUPER BORED AND WE HAVE TO GO NOW!

TELL HER TO SHUT UP.

BABY...

DON'T EVEN START WITH ME, STEPHEN!

THIS ISN'T AWKWARD AT ALL.

MAYBE WE SHOULD CLEAR OUT AND GIVE STEPHEN STILLS SOME SPACE.

THEY'RE GONNA TALK ABOUT ME!

YOUR CURRENT GIRL AND YOUR EX? NO KIDDING.

SHE'S NOT MY EX! ...WHAT DO YOU THINK THEY'RE TALKING ABOUT, THOUGH?

WELL, RIGHT NOW LISA IS EXPLAINING HOW YOU'RE A GIANT IDIOT. IN A MINUTE, RAMONA WILL SEE THE ERROR OF HER WAYS AND DUMP YOUR ASS.

AND WHAT, MARRY YOU?!

HEY, DUDE!

KNIVES CHAU?!

HOW'S IT GOING?

WH... WHEN DID YOU GET OLD ENOUGH TO GO IN A BAR?

KEEP IT DOWN!

WHERE'S JULIE?

ZIP

PEE

PEE

SPSH

TOILETS

STEPHEN!!

WHAT IS *SHE* DOING HERE?

I RAN INTO HER ON COLLEGE AND TOLD HER WE WERE ALL HANGING OUT. ARE YOUR PANTS TOO TIGHT, OR WHAT?

IT'S OKAY, JULIE!

DON'T *TALK* TO ME! HOW DO YOU EVEN KNOW MY *NAME?*

WHAT'S UP?

CAN WE GO?

WALLACE!?

WHAT ARE YOU DOING HERE? I THOUGHT YOU WERE GOING DANCING!

OH... I'M... STILL HERE?

YOU PRE-DRANK TOO MUCH AND FELL ASLEEP BEFORE EVEN GOING OUT! ISN'T THAT A FORM OF NARCOLEPSY?

I THOUGHT YOU'D BE GONE FOR ANOTHER COUPLE HOURS! I TOLD RAMONA WE COULD COME OVER HERE AND CUDDLE!

DROOP

BY ALL MEANS... *CUDDLE.* JUST... PRETEND I'M NOT HERE.

SO... UH... WANNA MAKE OUT?

22
Comes a time

Financial district
8:47 AM

MR. WELLS. IT'S A PLEASURE AS ALWAYS. WHAT CAN I HELP YOU WITH THIS MORNING?

Peter, their landlord
Kind of a scary guy

WELL, I—

I WASN'T REALLY LOOKING FOR AN ANSWER THERE.

I'LL GET RIGHT TO THE POINT, GENTLEMEN.

THE LANDLORD-TENANT RELATIONSHIP THAT WE SHARE HAS BEEN *STRAINED*, I'D SAY. IS THAT A FAIR ASSESSMENT?

Y...YES SIR.

SO *APPARENTLY*, YOU'RE ACTUALLY CAUGHT UP ON RENT.

BUT... THAT'S *IMPOSSIBLE!*

...BECAUSE YOU PAID FIRST-AND-LAST UP FRONT, AND *THIS IS YOUR LAST MONTH.*

ONE MILLION
HOURS LATER.

IS THAT LIKE A MORAL HIGH GROUND THING, OR ARE YOU JUST A PUSSY?

SMOKING IS... IT'S EVIL, RIGHT?

WHO SMOKES?

SO RAMONA STAYED HOME, EH? YOU DON'T THINK THAT'S A BAD SIGN?

SHE'S ALLOWED.

YOU WANT A PUFF?

HUH? UH... NO. I SAID NO, DIDN'T I?

St. Larson Catholic Primary School

St. Hope Larson Catholic Primary School

SCOTT...

YEAH?

YOU KNOW IN HIGH SCHOOL?

Y-YEAH?

HOW WE NEVER... WENT FOR IT? WELL... I...

LISA... YOU'RE DRUNK.

AM I SCOTT?

UH... I THINK SO, YEAH.

SLUMP

HEY... HAVE YOU CONSIDERED MOVING IN WITH HER? I ASSUME YOU CAN'T REALLY AFFORD YOUR OWN PLACE...

IF IT'S OUT OF THE QUESTION, DON'T EVEN WORRY ABOUT IT, GUY.

I'M JUST THINKING ABOUT YOUR OPTIONS, Y'KNOW?

NO, NO, IT'S... IT JUST HADN'T EVEN OCCURRED TO ME. I GUESS I'LL THINK ABOUT IT. I'LL TALK TO HER.

SCOTT, I'LL STAY IF YOU WANT ME TO STAY. I JUST WANT YOU TO CONSIDER THE POSSIBILITIES.

REMEMBER, WE HAVE TO MAKE UP OUR MINDS BY THE 27TH.

OH, YEAH, MY BIRTHDAY!

THE 27TH OF AUGUST, SCOTT.

NOT MY BIRTHDAY?

I'M AFRAID NOT.

SO WHAT? MAKE UP YOUR MIND. HOW HARD CAN IT BE?

YOU'RE A *MONSTER*, STEPHEN STILLS! THIS IS INSANELY DIFFICULT FOR ME!

C'MON, MAN, IT'S NOT A BIG DEAL.

I KNOW IT'S LIKE YOUR FIRST REAL PLACE AND ALL, BUT THESE SITUATIONS ARE TEMPORARY.

OH MY GOD, HIDE ME! IT'S THE GUY!

I'M SORRY, WHAT?

UH... DUDE?

SCOTT...?

We now join their conversation, already in progress...

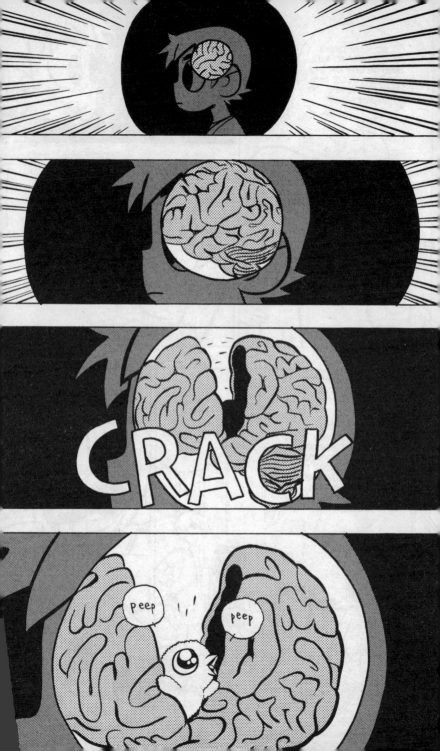

YOU AND HER?!

ROXANNE RICHTER
The 4th evil ex-boyfriend

I'M NOT A BOY!

OH, RELAX. IT WAS A PHASE.

I THOUGHT WE WEREN'T WEARING THESE THINGS ANYMORE...

YOU HAD A SEXY PHASE?!

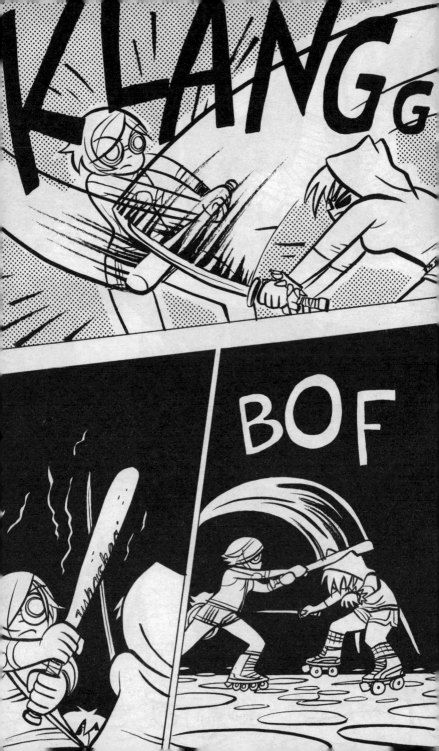

WHUP
KLOP
THIS SUCKS!
WHY ARE WE EVEN FIGHTING?!
BECAUSE YOU'RE A WHINY LITTLE BITCH?
YEAH!

HALF AIN'T GOOD ENOUGH, HUH?!

C'MON, YOU KNOW I DIDN'T MEAN IT LIKE—

GIVE IT A REST, RAMONA.

YOU'RE NOT MY MOM.

SHOVE

OW

WELL.

UM.

YEAH...

EDICAL ENTRE

YOU... *COULD*... TECHNICALLY... I SUPPOSE... UH... MOVE IN WITH *ME*. FOR A LITTLE WHILE, ANYWAY.

I MEAN I'D HAVE TO THINK ABOUT IT A *LOT*, BUT...

I GUESS THERE'S PROS AND CONS... YOU'RE KIND OF INCONVENIENT, BUT YOU HAVE A *JOB* NOW, RIGHT?

Nod nod

AND YOU DIDN'T EVEN BRAG ABOUT IT.

I KEPT FORGETTING TO.

DON'T TELL ME THAT!!

SNEAKY-DEE

SO WHAT'S UP, YOUNG NEIL?

WHAT DO YOU THINK IS UP? NOTHING'S UP! YOU ASSHOLES DON'T EVEN HANG OUT WITH ME ANYMORE!

IT'S NOT LIKE IT'S INTENTIONAL, MAN. YOU HAVE SUMMER CLASSES, AND WE HAVEN'T BEEN PRACTICING OVER AT OUR PLACE...

WHY HAVEN'T WE BEEN PRACTICING, ANYWAY?

...WE'RE RECORDING RIGHT NOW.

UM, SCOTT, I—

HE'S BEEN TURNING DOWN SHOWS, YOU KNOW. THE LADY WHO BOOKS SHOWS HERE KEEPS ASKING, AND HE KEEPS TURNING HER DOWN!

COME ON, THAT'S NOT FAIR.

EVEN IF I ADMIT I HAD A THING FOR HER, *WHICH I NEVER WILL*, IT'S ALL IN THE PAST. IT'S OVER!

IT'S OVER.

IF YOU'RE GONNA BE LIKE THIS, I—

GOODNIGHT, SCOTT.

IF YOU'RE GONNA BE LIKE THIS I'M GLAD SHE'S ONLY IN TOWN FOR A COUPLE MORE DAYS!

THAT'S ALL I WAS GONNA SAY! GIVE ME A BREAK!!

RAMONA, COME ON!!

(deep breath)

COME ON!!

YEAH, I DID.

WELL, UH... APPARENTLY YOU'RE FIRED FROM IT.

...OH.

SO HOW ABOUT THAT CAB FARE?

SURE, WHATEVER.

RUB RUB

THANKS, BUDDY.

HEY, CAN YOU GRAB MY TOOTHBRUSH AND LIKE A CLEAN SHIRT OR SOMETHING?

NO, I CAN'T. SORRY.

GO AWAY NOW.

27a

OH GOD WHY

THONK

CONTENTS OF SCOTT PILGRIM'S POCKETS

Lisa's sister's apartment

2 AM-ish

KEEP IT DOWN!!

MY SISTER HAS TO GET UP AT LIKE 5 AM, AND SHE'S A TOTAL BITCH ABOUT IT.

LOOK AT YOU! EVEN NOW!! I'M SO LUCKY!

OH, SHUT UP. IT'S JUST AN ORDINARY NIGHT-GOWN.

OH.

OKAY, NO, I PUT IT ON SPECIFICALLY AFTER YOU CALLED, ACTUALLY.

GOD, I'M SUCH A TRAMP!

LISA... WHAT'S THE DEAL WITH US?

YOU MEAN WHY DIDN'T WE...?

WELL, I MEAN, WHAT WAS GOING ON, LIKE, IN GENERAL?

WE DIDN'T KNOW *WHAT* WAS GOING ON. WE HAD ZERO COMPREHENSION. WE WERE PROBABLY TOO BUSY TRYING TO SEEM COOL.

MAN, YOU'RE RIGHT. I DIDN'T KNOW *ANYTHING*.

YOU KNOW...

YOU COULD HAVE *ASKED* ME IF I LIKED YOU.

DID YOU LIKE ME?

I DON'T WANT TO TALK ABOUT IT.

ANYWAY... YOU HAVE RAMONA NOW.

ENGGH.

AND YOU GUYS OBVIOUSLY HAVE SOMETHING SPECIAL.

I GUESS. I MEAN, WE HAVEN'T EVEN SAID THE L-WORD...

OH?

SHE'S COOL, BUT SHE HAS HER OWN ISSUES AND STUFF. SOME OF THEM ARE ACTUALLY PRETTY MUCH—

I MEAN, THEY'D BE DEALBREAKERS IF I WAS JUST A TINY BIT LESS INFATUATED, Y'KNOW?

SOME FOLKS HAVE A LOT OF BAGGAGE...

WE JUST HAD A FIGHT, TOO. A HUGE FIGHT.

DID YOU WIN?

UHH... NOT REALLY.

MAYBE
WE
SHOULD.

 WHA'D WE DO?

 HM?

 I'M A LITTLE OUT OF IT AND... I MEAN... WHAT DID WE *DO*?

 YOU MEAN DID WE MAKE OUT? DID WE "DO IT"?

D-DID WE?

NO, WE DIDN'T. BECAUSE YOU PUSHED ME AWAY AND STARTED BABBLING ABOUT HOW YOU'RE SO IN LOVE WITH RAMONA, AND I STARTED TO CRY, AND YOU TRIED TO CHEER ME UP, AND WE ORDERED A PIZZA AND GOT REALLY LOUD AND THEN MY SISTER CAME OUT AND *FREAKED* ON US.

SO WE SHUT UP, AND YOU FELL ASLEEP, AND I WENT BACK TO THE GUEST ROOM.

WHY DON'T I REMEMBER ALL THIS?

I DUNNO. YOU ATE A *LOT* OF PIZZA.

SO I ACTUALLY USED THE L-WORD?

GOD, YOU REALLY ARE IN LOVE WITH HER, AREN'T YOU? THIS IS SERIOUS.

I'M IN LOVE...?

ANYWAY, YOU CAN TELL HER THE TRUTH — THAT NOTHING EVER HAPPENED BETWEEN US, AND NOTHING EVER WILL. BLEH...

SIGH

• • •

PAH

LISA... I HAVE TO GO NOW.

DO YOU KNOW MY DAD?

HE'S, UH, TRYING TO KILL ME. PRETTY BADLY.

OHHH. HOW DID HE FIGURE OUT WHO YOU WERE?

UH, I WAS GONNA ASK *YOU* THAT, KNIVES.

HMM... WELL, A FEW WEEKS AGO WE HAD DINNER WITH MY AUNTIE, AND *SHE* SAID...

I SAW YOU WITH YOUR BOYFRIEND THE OTHER DAY, KNIVES, BUT YOU DIDN'T WAVE BACK.

HA HA HA, THAT'S NOT TRUE AT ALL!!

KNIVES, YOU MAKE OUT WITH BOY? *WHO?* STEPHEN CHOW?

NO, HE WAS *WHITE!* CUTE, TOO.

DOOM

I... GUESS... I... WAS... 100%... MISTAKEN.

HA HA! I'M TEN TIMES TOO YOUNG FOR A BOY- FRIEND, ANYWAY!!!

AND THAT MUST HAVE CAUSED MY DAD'S BRAIN TO...

SPLIT

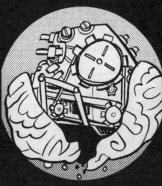

...BREAK IN HALF, REPLACED BY A PURELY MECHANICAL ENGINE OF REVENGE!

SO *HE* MUST BE THE ONE WHO DEFACED MY SHRINE!

SLASH

HE PROBABLY WANTS TO CUT YOUR HEAD OFF WITH HIS PRIZED ANTIQUE SAMURAI SWORDS!

MAN, MY DAD IS *SO* LAME.

WELL THAT'S JUST *GREAT.*

CRASH

SCOTT, I...

WHAT THE HELL IS THIS?

CLutch

RAMONA...

SCOTT?

I KNOW YOU JUST PLAY MYSTERIOUS AND ALOOF TO AVOID GETTING HURT. I KNOW YOU HAVE REASONS FOR NOT ANSWERING MY QUESTIONS.

AND I DON'T CARE ABOUT ANY OF THAT STUFF.

YOU... DON'T?

RAMONA, I'M IN LOVE WITH YOU.

LEVEL UP!

GUTS +2
HEART +3
SMARTS +1
WILL +1

NOW I'M GLAD I PICKED THAT LONGSWORD PROFICIENCY IN GRADE FIVE!

COME ON,
LITTLE MAN.
LET'S
DANCE.

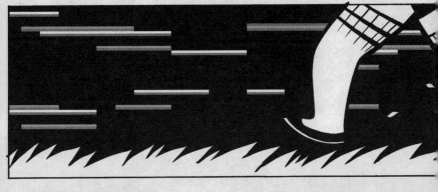

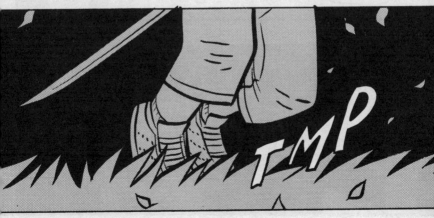

AT THE SAME TIME?

I DON'T HAVE TO ANSWER THAT!

AWW, MAN... AM I GONNA HAVE TO FIGHT TWO AT ONCE IN VOLUME 5?

...CAN THIS JUST BE THE LAST BOOK?

I NEVER SAID YOU WOULDN'T HAVE TO FIGHT TWO AT ONCE!

OH, SPEAKING OF WHICH... MR CHAU?

SIR, I NEVER HARMED YOUR DAUGHTER'S HONOUR. I ALWAYS RESPECTED HER, I HARDLY EVEN *TOUCHED* HER, AND I TRIED TO BEHAVE LIKE A...

THANKS FOR HELPING ME MOVE IN, YOU GUYS!

YEAH, WHATEVER.

I CAN'T BELIEVE YOU HAD THE *AUDACITY* TO CALL US OVER FOR *THIS.*

Ramona's apartment
(A few days later)

IS THIS SERIOUSLY YOUR ONLY BOX OF STUFF ASIDE FROM THOSE TWO GARBAGE BAGS? THAT'S KIND OF PATHETIC, MAN.

THERE'S ALSO THIS POSTER, IF YOU ACTUALLY WANT TO KEEP IT.

WHAT POSTER?

SCOTT

UH... THE IDIOTIC ONE? IT'S GOT GIRLS KISSING.

GLARE

The old apartment

...BECAUSE I SIGNED A LEASE ON A PLACE WITH MOBILE LIKE A WEEK AND A HALF AGO AND YOU WOULD HAVE BEEN *SERIOUSLY* SCREWED OVER IF YOU WANTED TO STAY!

HA HA HA HA HA HA HA HA

YOU BASTARD.

YEAH, SO, GIVE ME A CALL SOMETIME, BUDDY!

Chau residence

ARE YOU SURE?

I DON'T KNOW. I'M PRETTY SURE.

WELL... DO YOU LIKE HIM BACK?

I... I THINK SO. I MEAN—

AHEM

及 通常 在汉语中
有大量的量词 北
方方言的明显特点
包括 是种以孔子
时代所使用的以,
余皆不论

As far as I'm concerned, Scott Pilgrim is a halfway decent young man. Maybe you dating a white guy wouldn't be so bad.

WHAT WAS THAT ALL ABOUT?

MAN, I DUNNO, HE WAS SPEAKING *CHINESE* OR SOMETHING!

Kim's place

WAS THAT PERFECT?

SOUNDED PERFECT TO ME, MAN.

RIGHT ON! I TOTALLY ROCK!

YEAH, GREAT. I'LL REDO ALL YOUR PARTS AFTER YOU LEAVE, ANYWAY.

SO I GUESS WE'RE ALMOST DONE WITH THE ALBUM NOW!

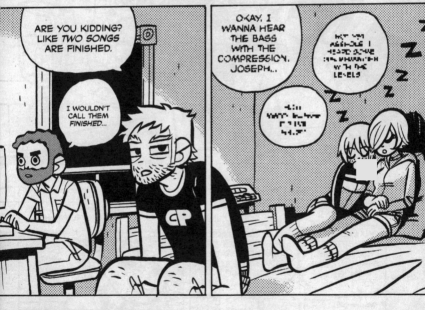

ARE YOU KIDDING? LIKE *TWO* SONGS ARE FINISHED.

I WOULDN'T CALL THEM *FINISHED*...

OKAY, I WANNA HEAR THE BASS WITH THE COMPRESSION, JOSEPH...

TO LISA AND HER CONTINUED SUCCESS!

HURRAH!

KOREAN DELITE

HOW OLD ARE YOU?

I'M 24. AND MY BIRTHDAY IS JANUARY FIRST. AMAZING, I KNOW.

NEW YEAR'S?! THAT'S... WAIT, YOU *SAID* AMAZING...

SO WHEN'S *YOUR* BIRTHDAY?

UH... SOON! IT'S THE 27TH.

UM, *SEPTEMBER* 27TH.

WE'LL BE THE SAME AGE!

NEXT: Twins!

Bryan Lee O'Malley has been alive since he
was born and will live until he dies, which will
probably be pretty soon. His dying wish will
be the wish that he hadn't wasted his best
years drawing this book.

His epitaph will be
whiny and narcissistic.

STOP
ARRÊT

This is the **back** of the book.
What do you think you're doing?
Who do you think you are?

Go to the other end of the book and start at page 1.
Your mother and I are very disappointed in you.

READING YOUR NEW GRAPHIC NOVEL: SOME OPTIONS

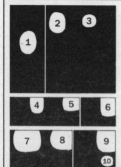

OPTION 1:
Follow the balloons from **left to right** and **top to bottom,** then move on to the next panel, the way you learned it at that sissy school of yours.

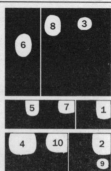

OPTION 2:
Read each balloon in whatever order appeals to you most. **Freestyle!** It's **your** book now! Don't let the **man** tell you which direction to read!

WARNING: For entertainment use only. Do not attempt to learn anything from this page.